CW00421578

Piano Mix 2

Great arrangements for easy piano

Grades 2–3

Compiled and edited by David Blackwell

ABRSM

INTRODUCTION

The purpose of this collection is to bring a selection of pieces from a wide range of non-piano repertoire – orchestral, chamber, operatic, ballet, choral and vocal – into the hands of early-grade pianists. A variety of non-classical pieces, including spirituals, folk songs, TV themes, marches and jazz pieces, completes the span of music plundered, and the whole is offered to introduce players to the riches of music in all its forms and – it is hoped – provide quality repertoire that will engage and enthuse. If it also encourages players to seek out the original or explore new areas of music, then so much the better.

A number of considerations have guided the approach taken in this anthology. Firstly, we have looked for pieces that are characterful and tuneful. A vital consideration is that the arrangement is pianistic and fits comfortably under the hands. Much care also has been taken to ensure that the pieces suit the grade levels given: the label 'Grades 2–3' means that the pieces are mostly at Grade 2 level, with a few pieces also included as an introduction to Grade 3. Allowing for some flexibility, pieces are printed in approximate order of difficulty. In all this, a balance has had to be struck between playability and faithfulness to the original. It is not possible to render every detail of a complex original in a simple piano arrangement, yet the intention is that arrangements are respectful even if not always exact, and retain a sense of completeness.

The practice of arranging music and reworking it for different instruments has a long and distinguished history. In the Renaissance period, contemporary songs and airs were decorated in transcriptions for keyboard, for example in the *Fitzwilliam Virginal Book*, while Baroque composers regularly reworked both their own compositions and the work of others to make new pieces. The popularity of the piano in the 19th century as a domestic instrument saw countless transcriptions of orchestral and chamber pieces for piano solo or duet; in an age before recordings and mass concert-going, it was a means of discovering and appreciating a wide repertoire of music. Performance of different repertoire on the piano remains a satisfying musical experience, and we hope that these new arrangements will provide pleasure and delight for pianists of all ages.

David Blackwell

I should like to thank the many arrangers who contributed to this collection, ABRSM staff Rosie Cousins, Carolyn Fuller, Robert Sargant and Nigel Scaife, and piano moderator Tim Barratt for all their help. I also offer heartfelt thanks to adviser Jan Bullard, whose many technical and musical suggestions helped polish and refine the arrangements. *DB*

First published in 2015 by ABRSM (Publishing) Ltd, a wholly owned subsidiary of ABRSM

Reprinted in 2017

© 2015 by The Associated Board of the Royal Schools of Music

All rights reserved. No part of this publication may be reproduced, recorded or transmitted in any form or by any means without the prior permission of the copyright owner.

Music origination by Julia Bovee
Cover by Vermillion
Printed in England by Halstan & Co. Ltd, Amersham, Bucks.
on materials from sustainable sources

CONTENTS

Jupiter

from *The Planets*, Op. 32

Arranged by Quintus Benziger

Gustav Holst
(1874–1934)

Gustav Holst was an English composer and teacher who for many years taught at St Paul's Girls' School, London. This piece is from his most famous work, *The Planets* suite for orchestra, which depicts in music the planets of our solar system. Within the movement for Jupiter, 'The Bringer of Jollity', lies this calm and beautiful melody.

Did you know? Holst's suite did not include a movement for Pluto, which was only discovered in 1930, 14 years after the work was completed. Pluto was downgraded to 'dwarf planet' in 2006.

© 2015 by The Associated Board of the Royal Schools of Music

Man is for the woman made

from *The Mock Marriage*, Z. 605

Arranged by Peter Gritton

Henry Purcell
(1659–95)

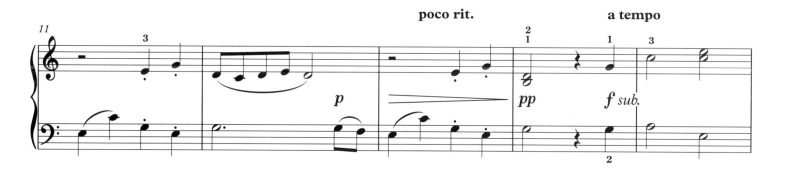

The English composer Henry Purcell wrote a lot of music for the theatre, including the opera *Dido and Aeneas* and songs and instrumental pieces for a large number of plays. This piece is a song Purcell wrote for *The Mock Marriage*, a play by Thomas Scott, first produced in London in 1695.

Did you know? When he played the organ at Westminster Abbey for the coronation of William and Mary in 1689, Purcell sold tickets for seats in the organ loft, from where spectators got a grandstand view! From this he made a profit of £35 – his annual salary as organist was £10.

© 2015 by The Associated Board of the Royal Schools of Music

Roaring Jelly

Arranged by Rory Boyle

Traditional Scottish

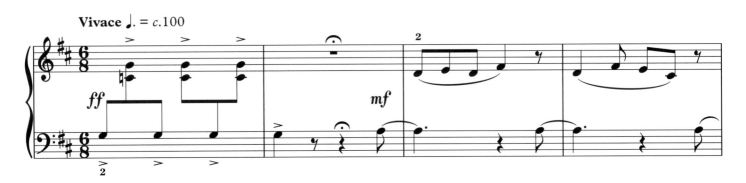

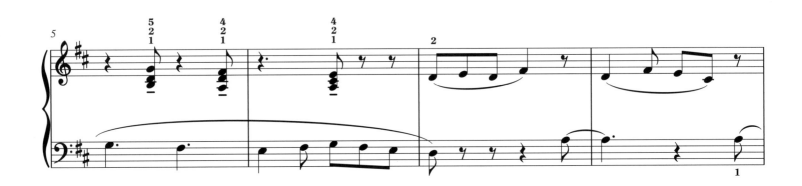

'Roaring Jelly' is a Scottish jig, also known as 'Smash the Windows'. It is likely that 'roaring' in the title refers to the rolling boil required for cooking jellies and jams. Like many dances of its kind, this tune shares a common Scottish and Irish origin.

Did you know? Gelignite (or 'gelly', pronounced 'jelly') was an explosive commonly used to blast rock in mines in Scotland in the last century. On some days, Scottish miners would use 'roaring gelly' by day, then dance to a tune with the same name at night!

© 2015 by The Associated Board of the Royal Schools of Music

Kangding Love Song

Arranged by Austin Yip

Traditional Chinese

This popular Chinese song is from the mountainous Kangding region of western Sichuan province in south-west China, close to the border with Tibet. It originated in the 1930s and was probably sung while local people worked on the mountain, gathering firewood and herding animals. The text first sets the scene – horses run on the mountains as the moon shines above – then celebrates youthful love.

Did you know? The melody of this tune is 'pentatonic', which means it only uses five notes: ACDEG in this piece. Many folk songs from around the world are pentatonic like this.

© 2015 by The Associated Board of the Royal Schools of Music

The New Trout

from Piano Quintet in A, D. 667, fourth movement

Arranged by Philippa Topham

Franz Schubert
(1797–1828)

The Austrian composer Franz Schubert is one of the most popular composers of the early 19th century. This piece is from his Piano Quintet in A, known as the 'Trout' Quintet because the fourth movement, on which this piece is based, is a set of variations on the tune from Schubert's song 'The Trout' (Die Forelle).

Did you know? Although in the song the trout is caught by the fisherman, the piano quintet is one of Schubert's sunniest compositions.

© 2015 by The Associated Board of the Royal Schools of Music

La Mourisque

Arranged by Martin White

Tylman Susato
(c.1510/15–c.1570)

Tylman Susato was a 16th-century composer, instrumentalist and music publisher who lived in the port city of Antwerp in the Low Countries (now Belgium), then one of the richest cities in Europe. This joyful piece is from a collection of dances he published in 1551.

Did you know? The address of Susato's publishing house in Antwerp was 'At the sign of the Crumhorn' – the crumhorn was a highly popular woodwind instrument of his day.

© 2015 by The Associated Board of the Royal Schools of Music

The Merry Villagers

from Peasant Cantata, BWV 212

Arranged by Anne Marshall

J. S. Bach
(1685–1750)

Johann Sebastian Bach was a German composer, now considered to be one of the greatest composers of Western music. This lively tune is from an unusual cantata (a work for voices and instruments), first performed in 1742 and written to celebrate the birthday of a local landowner. In this piece the villagers sing as they go to the local tavern to toast the landowner and listen to the bagpipes playing.

Did you know? Bach also wrote a cantata in praise of drinking coffee – the Coffee Cantata – which was first performed in a coffee shop in Leipzig.

© 2015 by The Associated Board of the Royal Schools of Music

Rondeau

from *Abdelazar*, Z. 570

Arranged by Nicholas Scott-Burt

Henry Purcell
(1659–95)

Henry Purcell was an English composer who wrote music for the Stuart court and also for the theatre. This piece is from the music Purcell wrote for a production of the play *Abdelazar, or The Moor's Revenge*, in 1695.

Did you know? The English composer Benjamin Britten used this music as the basis of his *Young Person's Guide to the Orchestra*, an orchestral work that introduces the sounds and capabilities of the different orchestral instruments.

© 2015 by The Associated Board of the Royal Schools of Music

Old Joe Clark

Arranged by Alan Bullard

Traditional American

This American fiddle tune records the lively adventures of Joe Clark, who was born in 1839, served briefly in the American Civil War, then took up farming in Kentucky. According to the song, his wife was '10 feet tall' and he lived in a house 'filled with chicken pie'.

Did you know? This tune is in the Mixolydian mode, which is the sequence of notes you get if you play up an octave on the white notes from G to G. It looks like G major, but there's no F sharp in the key signature!

© 2015 by The Associated Board of the Royal Schools of Music

Rondo

from Cello Concerto No. 2 in D, Hob. VIIb:2, third movement

Arranged by David Blackwell

Joseph Haydn
(1732–1809)

Joseph Haydn was an Austrian composer who wrote many famous works in many musical forms (including the symphony, string quartet and piano sonata) and who was treated as a celebrity on his visits to London in the 1790s. This cheerful melody is the main theme of the last movement of his Cello Concerto No. 2.

Did you know? A concerto is a work for a solo instrument (sometimes more than one) and orchestra, and provides an opportunity for the soloist to show what a good player he or she is!

© 2015 by The Associated Board of the Royal Schools of Music

Match of the Day

Arranged by Peter Gritton

Barry (Rhet) Stoller
(born 1945)

MOTD is one of the longest running shows on British television, having been on air since 1964. This music, which captures the excitement and energy of the football crowd, has been the theme tune since 1970, and is so well known that it instantly says 'football!'

Did you know? The closing fanfare (last four bars) was written first, and was intended by the composer to give the music a sense of gladiators entering the arena of the ancient Roman games.

© 1970 RAK Publishing Limited. This arrangement © 2015 RAK Publishing Limited.
All rights reserved. Used by permission.

Romance

from Piano Concerto No. 20 in D minor, K. 466, second movement

Arranged by Nancy Litten

W. A. Mozart
(1756–91)

The Austrian composer Wolfgang Amadeus Mozart was a child prodigy or genius, who from the age of six toured the cities and royal courts of Europe with his father and sister, playing concerts and writing music. This tender and serene melody opens the slow movement of his Piano Concerto No. 20, first performed in Vienna in 1785 with Mozart as the soloist.

Did you know? This movement is played in the final scene and end credits of *Amadeus*, Peter Shaffer's famous film about Mozart released in 1984.

© 2015 by The Associated Board of the Royal Schools of Music

Scherzo

from Serenade in D for String Trio, Op. 8

Arranged by David Blackwell

Ludwig van Beethoven
(1770–1827)

The German composer Ludwig van Beethoven is widely regarded as one of the greatest composers of all time. Despite losing his hearing, he continued to write many famous pieces. This lively tune is from his Serenade for three string instruments: violin, viola and cello.

Did you know? Scherzo, from the Italian word for 'joke' or 'game', is the name for a quick movement or piece, often with a light-hearted or playful character. Beethoven wrote a scherzo in place of the more traditional minuet in all but two of his symphonies, making it a lively, high-spirited movement, just like this piece.

© 2015 by The Associated Board of the Royal Schools of Music

March

from *L'Arlésienne*, Suite No. 1

Arranged by Alan Bullard

Georges Bizet
(1838-75)

Georges Bizet was a French composer who showed musical talent from a young age and entered the Paris Conservatoire of Music at the age of nine. This piece is from the music he wrote for the play *L'Arlésienne* ('The Girl from Arles'), staged in Paris in 1872. It is based on a traditional tune from the Provence region of south-east France.

Did you know? This piece was adopted as a military march by Enver Hoxha, who ruled Albania for 40 years following World War II.

© 2015 by The Associated Board of the Royal Schools of Music

Andante

from Trumpet Concerto in E flat, Hob. VIIe:1, second movement

Arranged by Martin White

Joseph Haydn
(1732–1809)

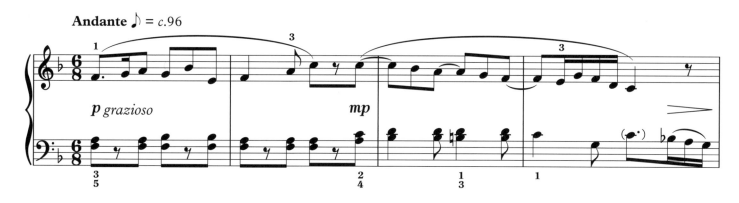

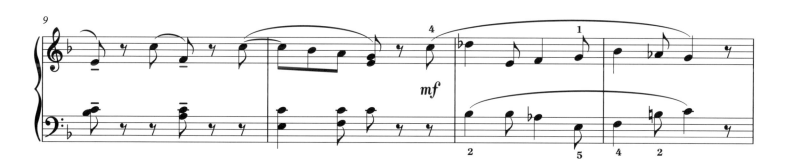

The Austrian Joseph Haydn was one of the most successful composers of the Classical period, a friend of Mozart (Mozart dedicated a set of six string quartets to him) and teacher of Beethoven. This is the slow movement of his Trumpet Concerto, one of the first pieces to be written for the new keyed trumpet, an invention that enabled many more notes to be played across the range of the instrument.

Did you know? The world's largest trumpet band gathered in 2006 in Oruro, Bolivia, when 1,166 trumpeters played together.

© 2015 by The Associated Board of the Royal Schools of Music

Largo

from Symphony No. 9 'From the New World'

Arranged by David Blackwell

Antonín Dvořák
(1841–1904)

This famous melody is from the slow movement of Antonín Dvořák's Symphony No. 9, written when the Czech composer was director of the National Conservatory of Music in New York from 1892 to 1895. The title of the symphony, 'From the New World', refers to the Americas.

Did you know? A recording of this symphony was taken to another new world in July 1969: as the American astronaut Neil Armstrong stepped on to the lunar surface during the Apollo 11 space mission to the Moon, he played a recording of this piece.

© 2015 by The Associated Board of the Royal Schools of Music

Low Bridge, Everybody Down

Arranged by Nikki Iles

Thomas S. Allen
(1876–1919)

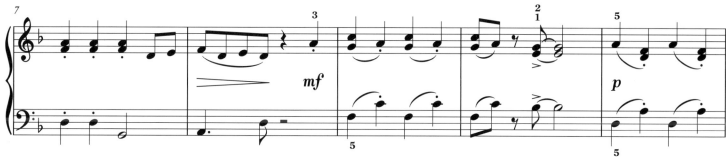

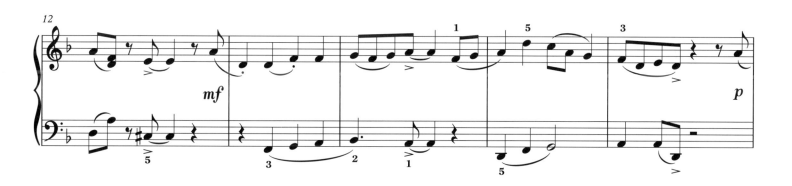

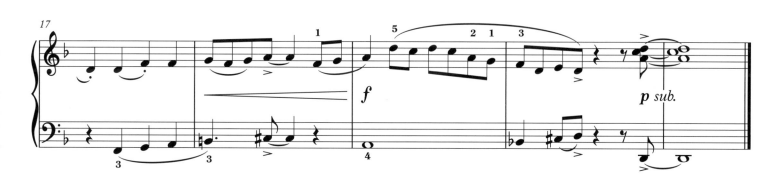

This song from 1905 is about barge traffic on the Erie Canal, which was built in the 19th century to connect New York City with Lake Erie, a distance of over 350 miles. As mules pulled the barges, travellers had to duck down each time they passed under a low bridge to avoid being knocked off.

Did you know? Thomas Allen, the composer of this song, also wrote music for the American vaudeville theatre – a form of variety entertainment involving musicians, comedians, acrobats and jugglers.

© 2015 by The Associated Board of the Royal Schools of Music

Entr'acte No. 3

from *Rosamunde*, D. 797

Arranged by Nicholas Scott-Burt

Franz Schubert
(1797–1828)

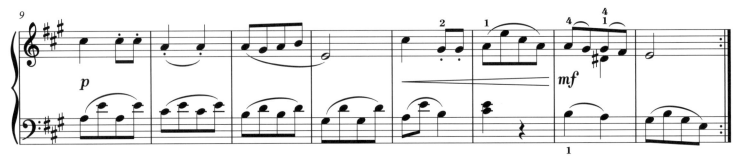

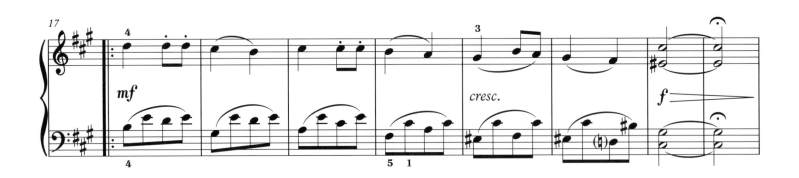

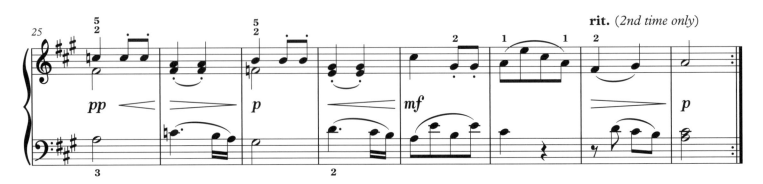

Franz Schubert was an Austrian composer who composed quickly and wrote a huge quantity of music: in one year (1815) he wrote an estimated 20,000 bars of music, including a symphony, 150 songs and many other pieces. This piece is from the music he wrote for the play *Rosamunde, Princess of Cyprus* in 1823. An 'Entr'acte' is a piece of music played 'between the acts' of a play or opera (from the French 'entre acte').

Did you know? Schubert liked this tune so much that he used it again in his String Quartet No. 13, and something very like it in his Impromptu in B flat for piano.

© 2015 by The Associated Board of the Royal Schools of Music

Oberek

Arranged by Alan Bullard

Traditional Polish

The Oberek is a lively Polish folk dance, and the fastest of the five national dances of Poland. Oberek comes from the Polish word meaning 'to spin', and the dance has many quick steps and turns. The music for folk dances would be played by the village band or *kapela*, which typically consisted of violin, drum and accordion.

Did you know? Although he did not name any pieces 'Oberek', the great Polish composer Fryderyk Chopin used the rhythms and character of the Oberek in several of his Mazurkas for piano.

© 2015 by The Associated Board of the Royal Schools of Music

The Liberty Bell

Arranged by Nicholas Scott-Burt

J. P. Sousa
(1854–1932)

John Philip Sousa was an American composer who wrote over 130 marches for brass and military band. This piece is one of Sousa's most famous marches and named after the huge bell in Philadelphia, Pennsylvania, that is a symbol of American independence. Inscribed with the words 'Proclaim Liberty', it was later used to rally abolitionists to the anti-slavery movement.

Did you know? The sousaphone, a large brass instrument that wraps round the player's body and is therefore well suited to being played while marching, is named after Sousa.

© 2015 by The Associated Board of the Royal Schools of Music

Allegretto

from Clarinet Quintet in A, K. 581, fourth movement

Arranged by Clem Virgo

W. A. Mozart
(1756–91)

The great composer Wolfgang Amadeus Mozart often became completely absorbed in one kind of composition. In 1775 he wrote a series of four violin concertos, and in 1788 composed his last three symphonies in quick succession. This is the theme from the last movement of his Clarinet Quintet (a work for clarinet and string quartet), written in 1789.

Did you know? The clarinet as we know it became popular at the end of the 18th century and Mozart, with this work and his Clarinet Concerto, wrote some of the earliest and greatest music for it.

© 2015 by The Associated Board of the Royal Schools of Music

In the Mood

Arranged by David Blackwell

Joe Garland
(1903–77)

Joe Garland was an American composer and arranger who wrote a number of jazz hits in the swing band era. Arranged as a high-spirited instrumental for the Glenn Miller band, the song became a number 1 hit in the 1940s, topping the US charts for 13 weeks.

Did you know? Glenn Miller and his famous band entertained US troops in England in World War II, giving over 800 performances, live in concert or on the radio. The band's music was a powerful morale booster to all those who heard it.

© 1939 Shapiro Bernstein & Co. Inc. This arrangement © 2015 Shapiro Bernstein & Co. Inc.
Shapiro Bernstein & Co. Limited, New York, NY 10022-5718. Reproduced by permission of Faber Music Ltd. All rights reserved.

Dance of the Reed Pipes

from *The Nutcracker*, Op. 71

Arranged by Nancy Litten

P. I. Tchaikovsky
(1840–93)

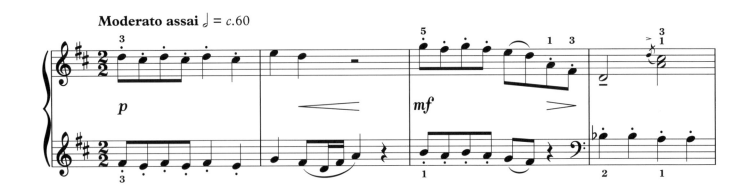

This famous dance is from Pyotr Il'yich Tchaikovsky's ballet *The Nutcracker* (1892), a fantasy tale set on Christmas Eve, in which a young girl rescues a wooden nutcracker from the Mouse King. The nutcracker is transformed into a prince and together they travel to a magical kingdom ruled by the Sugar Plum Fairy.

Did you know? Music from *The Nutcracker* has appeared in jazz, klezmer and rap versions, as well as in cartoons (Tom and Jerry, Mickey Mouse and The Simpsons), TV adverts and films, including Disney's *Fantasia* (1940).

© 2015 by The Associated Board of the Royal Schools of Music

The Kalendar Prince

from *Scheherazade*, Op. 35

Arranged by Alan Bullard

N. A. Rimsky-Korsakov
(1844–1908)

This piece, by the Russian composer Nikolay Andreyevich Rimsky-Korsakov, is from the orchestral work *Scheherazade*, a dazzling, colourful work based on the famous stories of The Arabian Nights. In these stories, the Sultan's wife, Scheherazade – represented by the tender melody in the first eight bars of this piece – delays her execution by telling exotic stories for 1,001 nights until the Sultan spares her life.

Did you know? Rimsky-Korsakov was an officer in the Russian navy, and brought his love of the sea to the first movement of *Scheherazade*, 'The Sea and Sinbad's Ship'.

© 2015 by The Associated Board of the Royal Schools of Music

The Muppet Show Theme

Arranged by David Blackwell

Jim Henson (1936-90) and
Sam Pottle (1934-78)

This is the theme tune of *The Muppet Show*, a hugely popular television puppet series produced in Britain between 1976 and 1981. Based on the long-running American series *Sesame Street*, the show featured Kermit the Frog, Miss Piggy, Gonzo, Fozzie Bear and a host of other characters.

Did you know? The fame of the Muppet characters has extended far beyond the TV series and they have appeared on chat shows, presented at the Oscars, made cameo appearances in films and sitcoms and helped raise money for UK charities Comic Relief and Children in Need.

© 1976 Fuzzy Muppet Songs administered by Artemis Muziekuitgeverij B.V. (for Europe) and Walt Disney Music Company (for World excluding Europe). This arrangement © 2015 Fuzzy Muppet Songs.
Warner/Chappell Artemis Music Ltd, London, W8 5DA. Walt Disney Music Group, Burbank, CA 91521, USA. Reproduced by permission of Faber Music Ltd. All rights reserved.